Contents

American Art Posters of the 1890s

modern Art

EDITED BY J. M. BOWLES
PUBLISHED BY L. PRANG & CO.

Arthur W Dow

American Art Posters of the 1890s

JOSEPH GODDU

November 25, 1989 to January 6, 1990

Hirschl & Adler Galleries
21 East 70th Street
New York, New York 10021
212 535-8810

Frontispiece
Arthur Wesley Dow
Modern Art. . . , 1895
Cat. 17

Overleaf
Will H. Bradley
BRADLEY HIS BOOK, 1896
Cat. 9

Library of Congress Cataloging-in
Publication Data

Goddu, Joseph

American Art Posters of the 1890s

ISBN 0–915057–32–8
        Bibliography: p. 78
        I. Posters, American—Catalogs.
2. Posters—19th Century—United
States—Catalogs. 3. Decoration and
ornament—United States—Art
Nouveau—Catalogs. 4. Posters—
New York (N.Y.)—Catalogs.
I. Hirschl & Adler Galleries, Inc.
II. Title   89–81468

© Hirschl & Adler Galleries, Inc.
21 East 70th Street
New York, New York 10021

Acknowledgments

This exhibition would not have been possible without the generous assistance of many individuals. First and foremost, I would like to thank the Director of the Department of American Prints at Hirschl & Adler, Janet A. Flint, whose advice and support has proved invaluable during the two years in which this exhibition has been in preparation. Douglas Dreishpoon was also immensely helpful, providing guidance in the production of the catalogue.

Others who loaned works, generously shared their expertise, or led me to material, include Tony Alvarez, Jack Banning, Merrill Berman, Bob Brown, Stuart Feld, Richard Flint, Stuart and Roberta Friedman, Carol Fruchter, Krystyna Goddu, George Goodstadt, Elizabeth Harris, Mr. and Mrs. Raymond Horowitz, David W. Kiehl, Scott Krawitz, Mr. and Mrs. H. Kurfirst, Leonard A. Lauder, Eric Layton, Ray Lazerson, Barbara Liebowits, Peter Max, Elena Millie, Susan Reinhold, Jack Rennert, James L. Reinish, Leslie and Alice Schreyer, Larry Shar, Lana and Shelley Speyer, Terry Shargel, Steven Thomas, Mary Tidwell, and Roberta Waddell.

As posters have traditionally been regarded more as ephemera than as fine art, they have often been mistreated by collectors and dealers unaware of advances made in the technology of paper conservation. Andrea Pitsch acted as consultant on these matters and provided faultless restoration, as needed, of works whose delicate nature demanded consummate expertise.

J G

Introduction

Pictures Meant to Be Seen by People Who Did Not Mean to See Them

This exhibition focuses on a brief, yet brilliant period in the history of American graphic art—that of the American art poster of the 1890s. Although the rise and decline of the poster movement spans a decade, it is the intensity of the "poster craze" that gripped the country from 1894 to 1896 which figures most prominently here—sixty-two of the eighty-two works were produced during this remarkable and richly creative period. A Hyatt Mayor's apt and arresting definition of pictorial posters—"pictures meant to be seen by people who did not mean to see them"[1]— reveals their primary function. Posters are the children of commerce. They are, first and foremost, an attempt to persuade.

Posters, then, are meant to perform; they are an *applied* art.[2] It is a discomforting term for the viewer unaccustomed to considering functional art forms. With a few exceptions, American posters of the 1890s have been ignored by art historians, whose training has left them ill-suited to the task of reconciling function with the rarefied world of form. Similarly, there has been no stampede among commercial art galleries to exhibit "advertising." However, a number of recent museum exhibitions have given us the opportunity to examine posters in a variety of contexts.[3] We are now in a better position to appreciate some of the non-commercial roles they fulfilled; and there were many.

During its brief reign, the art poster was an effective forum for the introduction of avant-garde aesthetics to the American public. Will Bradley's early posters are among the most powerful expressions of Art Nouveau realized in America. Edward Penfield's mature work exposed millions to the Post-Impressionist iconography of the Nabis. In addition, the poster gave numerous artists, including John Sloan and Maurice Prendergast, a paid chance to explore a new art form that had a guaranteed audience.[4]

The power of the poster to sell ideas—to educate—was fully understood by artists and critics of the time. Louis Rhead lectured on the "moral aspect of the artistic poster"[5] at the same time that many others were hailing the medium as an art form for the masses. Will Bradley's Wayside Press was an attempt to promote, by example, the philosophy of the Arts & Crafts Movement. Art posters, whether intentionally or not, also acted as agents for social and political change. The woman depicted in Penfield's poster for Stearns bicycles (Fig. 19) is not merely pretty, fashionable, and sophisticated; she is independent. Imagery of emancipation appealed to the self-image of well-to-do women with the money and time to take up the new sport of cycling.

If the study of the American art poster teaches us anything, it is that form and function need not translate as beauty and the beast. Function's demand of the poster—that it communicate forcefully and with an economy of means—did not restrict its potential as an art form. On the contrary, as many of the posters in this exhibition reveal, this requirement served to distill the aesthetic and philosophical aspirations of the artists who took up the medium, resulting in works of immense power and beauty.

Fig. 1

Will H. Bradley
THE/CHAP-/BOOK, 1894
Cat. 1

Fig. 2

Will H. Bradley
THE/MODERN POSTER. . . , 1895
Cat. 3

Fig. 3

Will H. Bradley
THE/CHAP/BOOK, 1895
Cat. 6

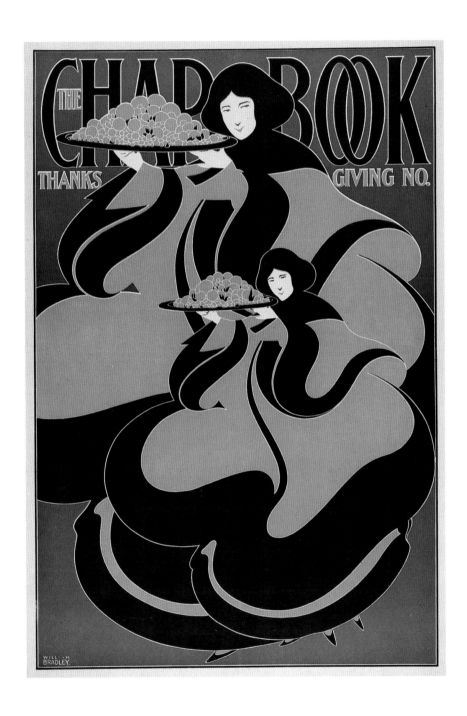

Fig. 4

Will H. Bradley
THE CHAP BOOK /
THANKSGIVING NO., 1895
Cat. 7

Fig. 5

William L. Carqueville
LIPPINCOTT'S/JULY, 1895
Cat. 13

Fig. 6

William L. Carqueville
LIPPINCOTT'S/NOVEMBER, 1895
Cat. 15

The Birth of an Art Form

The father of the art poster was the Frenchman Jules Chéret (1836–1932), who, like many later masters of the poster, had a thorough knowledge of the technical requirements of the print media in which he worked.[6] When Chéret established his own lithography firm in 1866, French technical expertise in color lithography lagged far behind that of Britain and the United States. The walls of Paris were plastered with black-and-white handbills advertising everything from ship departures to patent medicines in a mind-boggling jumble of type. Although in the 1830s some French publishing houses had begun to issue pictorial posters with black-and-white lithographs by book illustrators, such posters were the exception rather than the rule.

Chéret transformed the streets of Paris overnight with the introduction of picture posters brimming with color. He introduced an inexpensive three-color printing technique that employed transparent inks and a graduated background color, or *fond gradué*, to achieve intermediate tints of remarkable variety.[7] Eventually he increased the number of colors and developed a spatter technique, *crachis*, which became a favored device of poster artists through the 1890s. His images, drawing on influences as diverse as Tiepolo, Fragonard, and American circus posters,[8] featured bold, complex compositions and the "Chéret woman," a scantily clad beauty suspended magically within a three-dimensional space.

Through his command of stunning color effects and the use of evocative subject matter that emphasized atmosphere, rather than the actual product being advertised, Chéret introduced posters which were not meant to be *read*, but to be *seen*. The sensation his work caused is comparable only, perhaps, to the leap from radio to television in this century. Businesses soon scrambled to find artists and lithographers who could provide them with placards equal to those by the man Degas called "the Watteau of the streets."

As this new form of advertising proliferated, a critical literature arose,[9] providing historical background and aesthetic analysis. This literature, in turn, served to attract a body of collectors. The first poster exhibition was held in Paris in 1884,[10] and by 1886 the eminent book and print dealer Edmond Sagot was including posters in his sales catalogues. The first exhibition to provide a comprehensive survey of poster art was organized on the occasion of the Paris Universal Exhibition of 1889. France was by then firmly in the grip of a poster craze, and the stage was set for Bonnard and Lautrec to take up the form. In 1891, Chéret's posters and the book illustrations of Walter Crane were hanging alongside paintings by French and Belgian independent artists at the Salon des XX in Brussels—an indication of the respect accorded to applied graphics, in England and on the Continent, as a medium for the pursuit of a modern art.[11]

In America, the graphic arts were also poised to take the same step. Since the 1876 Centennial Exposition in Philadelphia, the applied arts had been undergoing a quiet revolution. It was at this exposition that Americans first encountered the English Arts & Crafts Movement and the decorative arts of Japan. Throughout the eighties, these influences had inspired and shaped the development of artisans working in pottery, embroidery, glass, the book arts, and interior design. At the beginning of the 1890s, the development of the art poster in America was lacking only one element—the commercial demand. In France ten years earlier, the entertainment industries had provided it. In America, the sponsors of the new commercial art would step forward from the world of publishing.

Fig. 7

Joseph J. Gould, Jr.
LIPPINCOTT'S/FEBRUARY, 1897
Cat. 20

Fig. 8

Joseph J. Gould, Jr.
LIPPINCOTT'S/JULY, 1897
Cat. 21

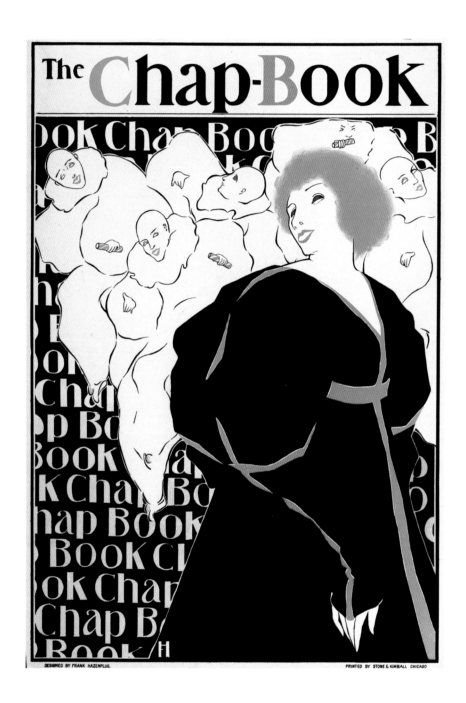

Fig. 9

Frank Hazenplug
The/Chap-Book, 1895
Cat. 22

Fig. 10

Herbert M. Lawrence
OCTOBER/CENTURY, 1895
Cat. 25

Fig. 11

Florence Lundborg
THE LARK/NOVEMBER, 1895
Cat. 27

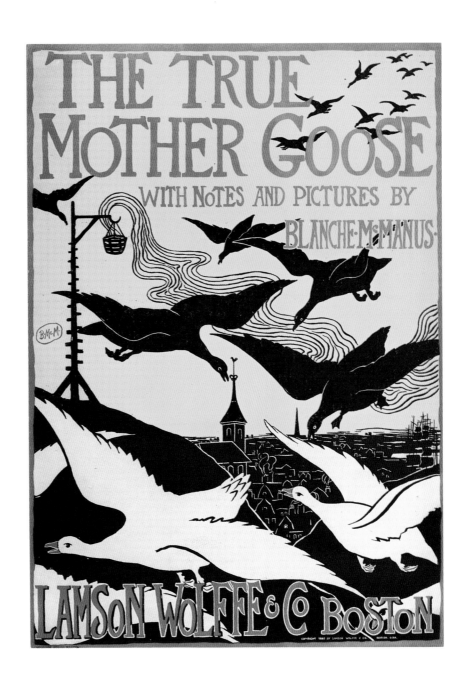

Fig. 12

Blanche McManus

THE TRUE/MOTHER GOOSE. . . , 1896

Cat. 32

American Beginnings

The final decades of the nineteenth century saw the rise of a prosperous middle class, the result of the rapid industrialization and urbanization that followed the end of the Civil War. (Chicago, for example, tripled in size between 1880 and 1890.) The new urban class devoted its increased leisure time to reading newspapers, books, and magazines as a means of self-improvement and self-education. The presses rolled in response.

Between 1870 and 1890, the combined circulation of American dailies rose 222 percent, while the population rose only 63 percent.[12] Technological advances in printing, which included the introduction of linotype and the rotary press, along with the development of economical papers manufactured from wood pulp, helped to fuel the growth of the publishing industries. With book, magazine, and newspaper publishers battling for their share of the middle-class dollar, advertising was seen as critical. Among the most effective weapons in the competition were illustrated placards, holiday covers, and special illustrated supplements. Some publishers, aware of the popularity of the poster in France, experimented with the medium as a promotional device. In 1882, the French artist Eugène Grasset was commissioned to design a cover for the Thanksgiving issue of *Frank Leslie's Illustrated Newspaper*. Seven years later, he provided a cover for the fashion weekly *Harper's Bazar* and posters for the Christmas issue of the monthly magazine *Harper's*. During this same year, Louis Rhead, an English artist who had come to America in 1883 to work for the publisher D. Appleton, designed holiday placards for *The Century Magazine* and *St. Nicholas*.[13]

In 1890, the Grolier Club held the first poster exhibition in America, composed primarily of French posters.[14] In September 1892, an article by Brander Matthews on "The Pictorial Poster" appeared in the *The Century Magazine* and helped legitimize the art form in this country. Matthews believed that the time was ripe for the development of the artistic poster, which he saw as the natural outgrowth of the growing Arts & Crafts Movement in America.[15] Six months later, following the success of a Christmas poster designed for *Harper's* by Eugène

Grasset, that firm decided to issue a new poster for each monthly issue of its magazine. Instead of commissioning a French artist, however, they turned to a member of the staff.

Edward Penfield, a young illustrator and art director, provided the inaugural poster for the April 1893 issue. The design was worked up at the last minute as "an experiment," in Penfield's words,[16] and contained the basic elements that would characterize the more than sixty *Harper's* posters that followed from his hand. A single figure or pair of figures, unmistakably upper class, were carefully integrated with the letters spelling out *Harper's* and placed, very often, against a flat plane of color. Penfield's subjects were usually engaged in a leisure activity associated with the season of the particular issue, or a witty reference might be made to the weather associated with a particular month.

A good description of Penfield's design for his first *Harper's* poster appeared in 1896 in the magazine *The Poster*: "It was a poster which forced itself upon one; in design and color it was striking, and yet it was supremely simple throughout. A very gentlemanly man walked down the salmon foreground arrayed in all the gorgeousness of a green driving coat. On his head was a light fore-and-after, and his gloves were 'London Tan.' The rain was falling all around him, but with charming nonchalance and flattering intentness he read a copy of *Harper's*."[17]

Penfield's design, widely considered the first American art poster, represented a radical departure from the old style magazine advertisement, which was often simply a listing of the table of contents. His bold, colorful, and clever images gave an oblique testament to the sophistication and social status required of the *Harper's* reader, and were most appreciated by precisely the segment of the public the magazine hoped to attract.

Fig. 13

Maxfield Parrish
THE CENTURY/Midsummer/
Holiday Number. . . , 1897
Cat. 34

Fig. 14

Maxfield Parrish
SCRIBNER'S FICTION NUM/BER, 1897
Cat. 35

Fig. 15

Edward Penfield
HARPER'S/MARCH, 1896
Cat. 40

Fig. 16

Edward Penfield
HARPER'S/JULY, 1896
Cat. 42

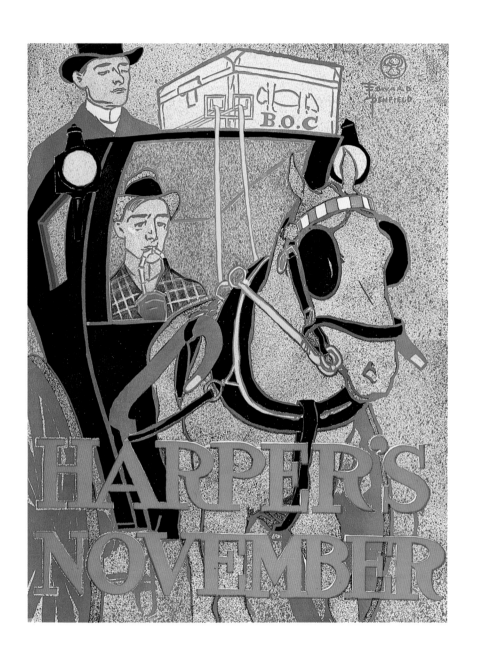

Fig. 17

Edward Penfield
HARPER'S/NOVEMBER, 1896
Cat. 44

Fig. 18

Edward Penfield
HARPER'S/CHRISTMAS, 1896
Cat. 45

By the end of 1893, other major publishing houses were jumping on the bandwagon, including J.B. Lippincott Co., Charles Scribner's Sons and The Century Co. Some periodicals, such as *Lippincott's*, followed the lead of *Harper's* and hired a single artist to provide their series of monthly posters. Will Carqueville, a Chicagoan who grew up in the shadow of the family printing presses, designed the posters for *Lippincott's* from December 1894 through 1895 (Figs. 5, 6). In 1896, J.J. Gould succeeded him; for the next two years, he created monthly poster designs in direct competition with *Harper's* (Figs. 7, 8). Other mainstream periodicals, such as *Scribner's* and *The Century Magazine*, commissioned their posters from a number of artists working in a variety of different styles, including Louis Rhead (Figs. 26, 34), Maxfield Parrish (Figs. 13, 14), Elisha Brown Bird and J.C. Leyendecker.

The poster fad was in full swing by 1895, with many publishers printing extra copies of their monthly placards for sale to a burgeoning collector's market. *The Modern Poster*, the first American book about the new medium, was published in that year (Fig. 2), and there were poster exhibitions in New York, Boston, Chicago, Denver, and elsewhere. The following year saw the birth of two periodicals, *The Poster* and *Poster Lore*, designed to cater to collectors in America and Canada. *The Poster*, in its inaugural issue, estimated their number at seven thousand. In Chicago there were "living poster shows," where participants would dress and pose to re-create the characters and tableaux of their favorite images, and W. Blackburn Harte reported in *The Fly Leaf*, "When a young man is in love, he no longer sends his heart's love a silly sentimental poem; he sends her a symbolic poster."[18]

Magazine publishers were not the only ones to recognize the commercial possibilities of the art poster. The new form of advertising was also enthusiastically adopted by a host of private literary presses and "little magazines" that appeared in the early 1890s as an outgrowth both of the rise of literacy and the spread of the Arts & Crafts Movement. The publication in 1891 of *The Story of the Glittering Plain*, by William Morris and his Kelmscott Press, along with the subsequent appearance on American bookstands of art journals such as *The Studio* and the

Yellow Book, renewed interest in the printing arts and provided the inspiration for the founding of hundreds of small publishing ventures all across America.[19] Most were started by idealistic young men who hoped to fulfill the Arts & Crafts ideal of integrating art and literature into everyday life by producing finely printed, affordable books and literary magazines. The use of artistic posters fell squarely within their philosophical aims and quickly became the primary means of advertising in an increasingly competitive market.

This sponsorship of poster design created a marriage of art and commerce which, at times, yielded spectacular results. The woodcut poster for the November 1895 issue of *The Lark* (Fig. 11) by the California artist Florence Lundborg is printed from the block she cut herself. Its execution is entirely in keeping with both its Japanese composition and with the philosophy espoused by the Guild of Arts and Crafts in San Francisco. The successful integration of text and image assured that the poster would fulfill its role as advertising. But this functional requirement did not prevent Lundborg from using a visual grammar as radically modern as any being explored by American artists of the time, in any medium.

Just how ubiquitous the independent and often idiosyncratic presses became in the mid-nineties can be inferred from a comment made by Elbert Hubbard, founder of the Roycrofters' own journal *The Philistine*: "We now have the *Lotus*, *Lotos*, and *Lettuce*. The latest is the *Prairie Dog*. Its hole is in Lawrence, Kansas and it is patterned after *The Chipmunk*. Verily, like begets like."[20]

The Chicago journal *The Chap-Book* was the best known of the little magazines, or "dinkey books," as they were called. It was started in 1894 by a pair of Harvard students, Herbert Stone and Ingalls Kimball, on the eve of their graduation. Intended originally as a simple newsletter to advertise the books they published, it grew to include observations on contemporary literature and the arts scene. Unlike establishment magazines such as *Harper's*, Stone and Kimball could afford to be bolder in the designs they used for advertising, and the posters they commissioned for *The Chap-Book* are among the most aesthetically daring works of the period.

Will Bradley, perhaps the most talented and original American artist to work in the poster medium, designed seven placards for *The Chap-Book* during 1894–95. His works of this period, such as the design for the 1895 Thanksgiving number (Fig. 4), are among the earliest and most fully realized expressions of the Art Nouveau style in America. They were certainly a major departure from the Victorian, highly realistic portraits of products that graced most store windows, trade signs, and business placards and, as such, did not sit well with some members of the captive public audience. A poem satirizing the "poster style," which appeared in the February 1895 *Harper's*, might have had Bradley's *Chap-Book* poster "The Blue Lady" (Fig. 1) in mind:

> *You must draw a dame with awful angularity*
> *In a landscape of geometry run mad;*
> *Give her frock a sweep with long particularity,*
> *And a pattern no raiment ever had.*
> *Oh, the sky it must be green, and the tree it must be blue!*
> *And the lake must look a claret-colored bubble;*
> *And a foreground must be found*
> *That can be a far background*
> *But a fashionable poster's worth the trouble!*[21]

In 1896, Bradley left for Springfield, Massachusetts, to establish his Wayside Press, a workshop of the printing arts in the Kelmscott tradition. The *Chap-Book* posters that followed were designed by different artists, most notable among them Elisha Brown Bird, Frank Hazenplug, and Claude Fayette Bragdon.

Along with the magazine publishers, book publishers large and small depended on posters as the most effective way to publicize new titles. The young and gifted Ethel Reed created a fine series of designs for the Boston firm of Lamson, Wolffe, & Co., as did Blanche McManus (Fig. 12). Copeland and Day commissioned designs for posters, illustrations, and book jackets from artists as diverse as Louis Rhead, John Sloan (Fig. 38), and Ethel Reed (Figs. 31, 32). Other artists whose work graced bookshop windows include Will Bradley, Maurice Prendergast, John Stewardson, and John Henry Twachtman.

Few industries outside of those related to printing and publishing took to art posters as a means of advertising—with one major exception. The craze for posters was eclipsed by another fad during the nineties—the craze for bicycles. Two technological advancements of a rather fundamental nature resulted in what was dubbed, relative to its predecessors, the "safety bicycle." They were the introduction of pneumatic tires and the replacement of the towering front wheel with front and back wheels of matched radii. Bicycling became the rage overnight, particularly among women with the education, means, and leisure to appreciate the sport's emancipatory possibilities. Not only could they participate on equal footing with their male counterparts, but the bicycle also provided them with a socially acceptable means of traveling independently.

By 1895, thirty publications had appeared devoted to bicycling,[22] and posters such as Charles Cox's for the magazine *Bearings* were an important means for increasing circulation (cat. 16). Bicycle manufacturers shrewd enough to recognize the appeal of the art poster to those wealthy enough to afford their wares commissioned designs from the best artists in the medium (cats. 11, 46, 59). The scale of these posters was usually larger than those produced by the publishing industry, in keeping with the amount of display space likely to be available on the walls of bicycle shops.

Coverage of American poster artists in contemporary newspapers and magazines of the day was extensive, and before long many publications were offering posters to collectors and earning handsome profits from the trade. By 1896, posters designed for *The Chap-Book* were being sold by that journal for ten times the newsstand price of 5 cents. It is fitting testimony to the American entrepreneurial spirit that a magazine could earn money by promoting the advertising designs that promoted the magazine in the first place. Yet, in the long run, the relationship between collector and advertiser was not symbiotic, even at the height of the poster's popularity. The January 1896 issue of *Poster Lore* observed:

> The day has passed when posters can be obtained of the newsmen and booksellers for the asking. So great is the demand that in many cases they do not serve their purpose as advertisements, but are reserved for regular customers who pay prices ranging from 5 cents to $1.00.[23]

Fig. 19

Edward Penfield
Ride a/STEARNS/and be/content, 1896
Cat. 46

Fig. 20

Edward Penfield
WESTERN/LAWN/1896/TENNIS/
TOURNAMENT. . . , 1896
Cat. 47

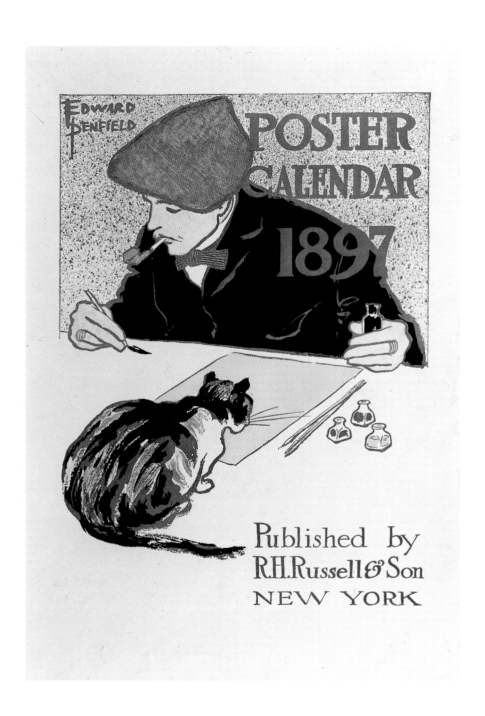

Fig. 21

Edward Penfield
POSTER/CALENDAR/1897..., 1896
Cat. 48

Fig. 22

Edward Penfield

[Poster Calendar for 1897], 1896

Cat. 49b

Fig. 23

Edward Penfield
[Poster Calendar for 1897], 1896
Cat. 49c

Fig. 24

Edward Penfield
[Poster Calendar for 1897], 1896
Cat. 49d

Fig. 25

Edward Penfield
[Poster Calendar for 1897], 1896
Cat. 49e

American Poster Styles

Americans made their own indigenous contributions to the stylistic development of the art poster. Their designs reflect an awareness of the numerous aesthetic movements, international in their influence, that appeared during the nineties. Common to all of these styles was the powerful effect of Japonisme.

One style, which found its most extreme expression among the group of Parisian Post-Impressionists known as the Nabis, appears by 1891 in posters by Lautrec and Bonnard. They employed the single-plane perspective, asymmetrical compositions, expressive line, and sharp contrasts of the Japonisme aesthetic in depictions of urban street life that were the Western equivalent of the "floating world" of wine, women, and song in the Ukiyo-e print. This style would find a more conservative expression in the works of Steinlen and Penfield a few years later.[24]

Penfield's early works were simple illustrations, executed in the conservative manner the public had come to expect of advertising and the newsweeklies throughout the seventies and eighties. Like Chéret's figures, Penfield's were fully modeled, product in hand, and set within a three-dimensional space, creating a tension with the flat text that would not be resolved until his later works. Beginning in 1896, however, Penfield moved away from strict representation, gradually adopting a more abstract vocabulary. The illusion of depth became a secondary concern in compositions whose bold patterns, strong flowing outlines, and bright, flat areas of colors interact within the frontal picture plane. Text and image were more easily integrated as equivalent formal elements, and the requisite copy of *Harper's* disappears from the hands of the depicted figures.

Penfield, like his French counterparts, was a master draftsman, and he shared their ability to caricature fashionable urban types through spare yet expressive line. His designs, however, and those of other Americans working in a similar style, such as Will Carqueville and J.J. Gould, are simpler than those of the French artists and present the viewer with characters and vignettes that are uniquely American. All three artists tended to be more adventurous in their employment of color than the French, who made greater use of the unprinted portion of the paper as a compositional element.

Penfield has been accused of imitating his contemporaries in Paris, but except for a few instances of direct borrowing of a motif,[25] the charge is unmerited. The development of Penfield's style owed as much to an art director's understanding of the qualities required of a successful advertisement—"It is more a question of what to leave out than of what to put in"[26]—and to his own appreciation of the constraints of the pressroom as it did to his knowledge of developments in poster art overseas.[27]

Another contemporary movement, Art Nouveau, burst upon the international scene at the same moment that the art poster caught hold in this country, and its radically new vision found a powerful proponent in the posters of Will Bradley. The language of Art Nouveau was not descriptive, but symbolic. Gone was the narrative, or vignette, which was an integral part of a Lautrec or Penfield poster. Form, color, and line were considered to have intrinsic emotional qualities distinct from their capacity to represent objects. Decoration and type gained in importance and were explored for their evocative potential as independent formal elements.

Bradley's earliest posters, such as his design advertising the publication of Tom Hall's *When Hearts Are Trumps*, reveal the strong influence of the English artist Aubrey Beardsley, who had been the subject of articles in *The Studio* and whose magazine *The Yellow Book* appeared in the United States in the spring of 1894.[28] Bradley's poster for the Thanksgiving number of *The Chap-Book* (Fig. 4) shows his complete mastery of the Art Nouveau style, with its flowing lines, rhythmic patterns, and contrasting flat color forms. Again as in Art Nouveau, the relation of subject to ground is often ambiguous; sometimes the two are locked together by a strong pattern within a flat plane (cat. 4). Ornamental motifs might be used to unify the composition (Fig. 3), and type forms often echo the contours of his subjects (Fig. 1). Bradley's importance to the movement was recognized internationally, and in 1895 his posters were included by Sigfried Bing in the opening exhibition of his L'Art Nouveau gallery in Paris.[29]

Bradley was also influenced early on by the philosophy and aesthetic dictates of the Arts & Crafts Movement. In 1892, he attended a lecture in Chicago given by

Fig. 26

Louis J. Rhead
CENTURY/MAGAZINE/MIDSUMMER
HOLIDAY NUMBER. . . , 1894
Cat. 68

Walter Crane, the British designer and book illustrator who was an ardent spokesman for the cause, and Bradley's own ties with the publishing industry assured his early exposure to the works of William Morris and the Kelmscott Press. The Kelmscott influence can be seen in Bradley's use of medieval motifs, as in his *Chap-Book* poster "Poet and His Lady" and in the woodcut decorated borders of his poster for *Bradley: His Book* (cat. 9, illus. p. 6).

This poster, also known as *The Kiss*, is considered by many to be Bradley's best and shows how effortlessly he was able to combine a variety of influences to create a uniquely personal product. The Kelmscott border frames the popular Pre-Raphaelite motif of a maiden and peacock, elegantly rendered in Art Nouveau line and pattern. This is not a poster that could have been produced in London or Paris. The stylistic synthesis, scale, primary color scheme, and aggressively expressive line represent a characteristically American response to aesthetic currents that were crossing international borders with increasing speed and ease.

Louis Rhead was another artist with strong ties to the English Arts & Crafts Movement, having received his training at the South Kensington Art School. He had a deep interest in the art and philosophy of the Pre-Raphaelites, which was reflected both in the style and motifs he employed, as well as in his belief in the moral and ethical ramifications of the poster as an art form for the common man. His poster for the mid-summer holiday number of *The Century Magazine* (Fig. 26) has all the hallmarks of his style. A pure, idealized female figure in medieval dress is placed in a natural setting composed of strong, curvilinear contours that outline unshaded areas of color. Rhead's work tends to have an overall decorative effect that could take on a distinctly Art Nouveau flavor, as in the design used to advertise *Le Journal de la Beauté* (Fig. 35).

Ethel Reed, like Bradley and Rhead, worked within the Boston publishing scene, and her posters reflect the same English precedents. She developed a distinct style, however, employing a painterly, fluid line and compositions that effectively meld her subjects with a decorative motif, usually floral (Fig. 31).

Toward the end of the decade, more realistic, fully modeled illustration came back into fashion, as in the work of Maxfield Parrish. By 1900, style in illustration and poster design had turned full circle as a result of this vogue for realism. It was a trend that may have been prompted by the increasing use of halftone reproduction techniques in the books and magazines the posters were intended to sell.

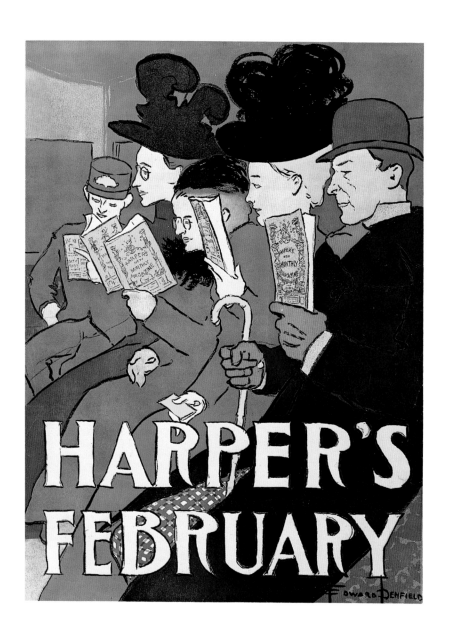

Fig. 27

Edward Penfield
HARPER'S/FEBRUARY, 1897
Cat. 50

Fig. 28

Edward Penfield

The/NORTHAMPTON. . . , about 1899

Cat. 59

Fig. 29

Edward Penfield
HARPER'S/MARCH, 1897
Cat. 51

Fig. 30

Edward Penfield
HARPER'S/AUGUST, 1897
Cat. 53

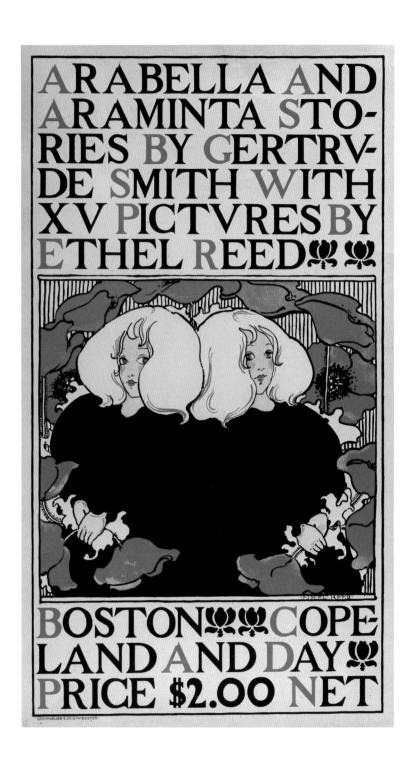

Fig. 31

Ethel Reed
ARABELLA AND/ARAMINTA. . . , 1895
Cat. 61

Fig. 32

Ethel Reed
In Childhood's Country. . . , 1896
Cat. 67

The Role of Technology and the Constraints of Commerce

Submission to the necessities imposed by a tool is no more a curb on genius than the grammar of a language. Genius will mold the method to its manner. FRANK WEITENKAMPF[30]

The stylistic grammar required of the poster artists would be determined not only by the many different reproduction methods in use at the time, but by the functional requirements of successful advertising as well. Because advertising had to be cost-effective, a poster had to be inexpensive to produce; hence, it had to be simple. Set-up time for multiple color runs on a press was expensive. When *The Century Magazine* held its poster contest in 1896, the rules of entry had nothing to say to the prospective entrants about subject matter or style. They were advised, instead, that the judges would be asked "to consider the effectiveness of the posters from the advertising standpoint, and the ease and cheapness with which they can be reproduced." It was said that Maxfield Parrish had to settle for second prize because his design required four colors instead of the three employed by the winning entry.[31]

As Penfield well understood, "effectiveness from an advertising standpoint" meant that a poster had to state its message clearly and simply. "A poster should tell its story at once—a design that needs study is not a poster, no matter how well it is executed."[32]

The two commercial constraints, ease of production and simplicity of means, sat well with the aesthetic imperatives of the day, and for good reason. In assimilating Japonisme, Western artists had not only adopted a new aesthetic, but a number of technological artifacts as well. The most characteristic stylistic elements of the Japanese print—its flat color planes and strong, expressive outlines—were the result of the technical limitations of color woodcut printing. Color schemes had to be distilled to their simplest, given the labor-intensive nature of block cutting and printing. The key block, which provided the contours of the subject and the matrix for the color sections to follow, had to be carved as a wide ridge in order to withstand repeated printings. These resultant stylistic traits would receive a second life as hallmarks of the poster style, no doubt because they were also well suited to the requirements of the pressroom in the 1890s.

The simplest and cheapest color effects to reproduce and print are flat areas. Will Bradley, using two inks, could achieve a varied palette by overlapping them and by making use of the unprinted portion of the page. He also would use pattern as a means of creating color effects of great complexity from just two colors, as in his poster for *The Chap-Book* of May 1895 (cat. 4). Bradley's facility with surface pattern developed during his training as a wood engraver. For the engraver working in black and white, the biggest challenge was to re-create the effect of two opposing colors of equal value. To a color-blind person they register as the same dull gray. To the engraver working in a color-blind medium, they are a nightmare. The only option is to render them as contrasting patterns, a compositional device Bradley brought to his poster designs, to astonishing effect.

Another means of achieving complex color effects was to vary the texture of a printed color. Chéret's inventions in this regard have already been mentioned. Both he and Lautrec created textures by spattering lithographic ink directly on the lithostone or by using grease crayons of varying hardness to create patterns and granular effects. They took advantage of the fact that colors register differently on different grounds: an ink that appeared bright blue as a solid on the blank sheet could change radically when applied as a light spatter grain over another color.

American poster artists followed the lead of their French counterparts, but expanded their vocabulary by making use of contemporary developments in photoreproduction. The transfer of images to printing surfaces coated with a photo-sensitive emulsion, which allowed the transfer of an artist's work to a relief block or lithostone without the intervention of a copyist, was a common commercial practice by the late eighties.[33] Photography also gave artists the freedom to work up an original design in whatever scale suited them, with the knowledge that the image could be reduced or enlarged to meet the exact requirements of the publisher. The grains and textures an artist could create on a sheet of paper with charcoal, crayon, paint, or pen could simply be photographed and transferred to the printing surface.

Edward Penfield's posters reveal the full inventory of techniques used by American artists of the mid-nineties to tease texture and graduated colors from evenly applied inks. As Will Bradley noted, Penfield's creativity in this regard was remarkable: "In methods of reproduction, that difficult point to which so few give even a passing thought, he is a past master. It is not within the scope of this article to tell how all this is effected, and yet the preparation of one color upon charcoal paper, and another color in spatter work and crayon upon another kind of paper, the hammering of a stipple in the metal plate, are all matters worthy of thought."[34]

Penfield's methods can be inferred from existing drawings (cat. 56) and from the accounts of contemporary witnesses.[35] Much like the Japanese artists who preceded him, Penfield would often pick a single color to act, in effect, as a key block. The design on this plate, or stone, would provide the outlines of the image and lettering, and a good deal of the tonal variety, which would be achieved through textures such as spatter work, prepared grains or mechanical rules, crayon work, and so forth. Penfield would work up the composition of this plate methodically in black and white, progressing from pencil sketch to outline drawing in ink, using pen and brush. Next, different tonal areas would be created with varying textures or patterns until the image was fully realized. Lettering would be added next, and any spatter work or drawing beneath the outline of the text would be eliminated with Chinese white.

The mechanicals for the two or three other colors were often directly made up by hand, rather than by transferring the photograph of a finished drawing onto a plate. This could be done by laying tracing paper over the finished key block design, since the secondary plates tended to be flat color areas with little or no modulation. Preliminary watercolor sketches would indicate the colors to be used, but Penfield mixed the inks for each poster run right in the pressroom and kept watch over his printers during set-up until the correct color settings had been achieved.

Other artists were also intimately involved in the printing of their poster designs. As mentioned earlier, Florence Lundborg, in keeping with Arts & Crafts tenets, cut the blocks for all but one of her posters herself. Will Bradley adapted Kelmscott principles of design for use in his own fully mechanized workshop. Even if his methods were not quite in tune with the philosophy of William Morris, his concern with quality craftsmanship was unflagging: his posters were meant to function not only as announcements for the latest issues of his magazine, but as advertisements for the services of his Wayside Press as well. He was more than willing to subcontract discrete production tasks to outside shops when the project merited it,[36] but the end result was always characterized by faultless presswork and unity of design.

Some poster artists, however, had minimal involvement in the production of their posters. By 1890, the assimilation of photoreproductive processes in commercial printing gave designers the freedom to work in whatever medium they wanted when developing their ideas, independent of the printing method employed by their publishers (cats. 18, 19). The artist could afford to remain ignorant of the technical procedures because the publisher's highly skilled staff was ready to make the translation from drawing to printed poster. Louis Rhead once dropped off a sketch in his publisher's mailbox on his way to the country, and only saw the color of the paper and inks in the completed poster upon his return a few weeks later.[37] The degree of collaboration between poster artists and their publishers and printers thus varied tremendously. As a general rule, the contributions made by a printing firm charged with realizing a poster design were, as Sinclair Hitchings has noted, "evolutionary, rather then reproductive."[38]

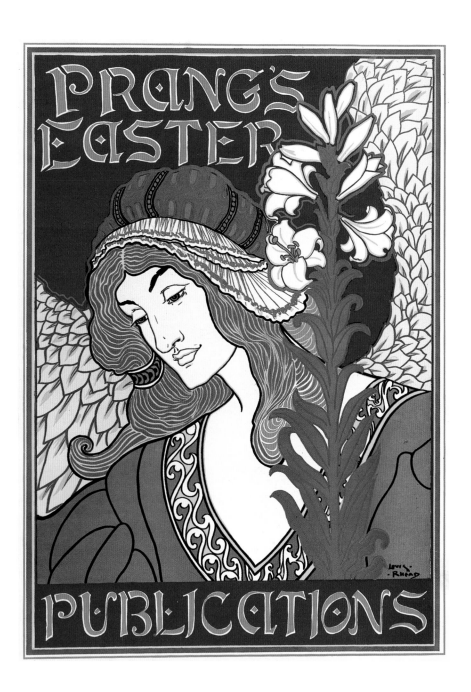

Fig. 33

Louis J. Rhead
PRANG'S/EASTER/PUBLICATIONS,
1895
Cat. 70

Fig. 34

Louis J. Rhead
SCRIBNER'S/FOR XMAS, 1895
Cat. 73

The Decline of a Commercial Art Form

As *Poster Lore* noted in 1896, once posters became collectible, they became inefficient as a means of advertising. Booksellers discovered early on what publishers would learn later—that the money the public spent on posters was often at the expense of book sales. By the late nineties, publishers had resolved the conflict by moving the coveted designs from the posters to the book jackets and magazine covers. Now the potential poster collector would, of necessity, have to become a book collector as well.[39] Also contributing to the rapid decline of the art poster was the ephemeral nature of most of the small art and literary journals that had done so much to promote the form. In 1896, they numbered about one hundred; by 1897, most were out of business. Moreover, public interest declined; the very intensity of the phenomenon, noted a contemporary critic, seemed to guarantee its rapid demise: "The American people have about run the poster craze into the ground, and I think the public will soon, if they have not already done so, begin to tire of the whole subject."[40]

Many artists managed the transition from poster design to cover design and book illustration with little trouble, including Edward Penfield, Will Bradley, Will Carqueville, Maxfield Parrish, and Louis Rhead. Some artists, such as John Sloan, Maurice Prendergast, William Glackens, and Claude Fayette Bragdon, dedicated increasing amounts of time to painting or other disciplines, gradually leaving commercial art behind altogether. Yet others, among them Ethel Reed and J.J. Gould, seemed to vanish from view as quickly as the posters themselves.

Function was primary to the genesis and development of the art poster of the 1890s. Rather than restrict its potential as an art form, however, the medium's commercial application freed it from constraints inherent in non-applied disciplines. The art poster was blind to academic tradition and to the background and training of the artists who took it up. As fertile ground for those who wished to test avant-garde principles, it led to new ways of seeing, and the medium accepted contributions from architects and interior designers as readily as it did from painters and graphic designers. Although economic factors dictated a simplicity of means, they also encouraged art and technology to meet in unprecedented ways, which in turn led to new modes of expression.

As an applied art, the art poster also required its creator to communicate clearly and directly. The medium thus distilled the aesthetic and philosophical aspirations of the day while creating works of stunning visual force. The artist Claude Fayette Bragdon recognized in the poster movement the potential for "a renaissance in which the spirit of the century, which is so largely a commercial one, will find an utterance in beauty instead of ugliness."[41] For a brief, yet glorious period nearly a century ago those aspirations were realized, in works whose legacy provides a rich addition to the history of American Art.

JOSEPH GODDU

59

Notes

1. A. Hyatt Mayor, *Prints & People: A Social History of Printed Pictures* (New York: The Metropolitan Museum of Art, 1971), no. 640.

2. For excellent surveys of the American posters of this period, see Edgar Breitenbach and Margaret Cogswell, *The American Poster* (New York: American Federation of Arts, 1967); The Metropolitan Museum of Art, *American Art Posters of the 1890s in The Metropolitan Museum of Art* (New York: The Metropolitan Museum of Art, 1987); and Roberta Waddell Wong, *American Posters of the Nineties*, exh. cat. (Boston: Boston Public Library, et al., 1974).

3. Museums devoting exhibitions to the American art poster within the last three years include The Metropolitan Museum of Art, the Santa Barbara Museum of Art, and the Hood Museum of Art at Dartmouth College. Survey exhibitions examining the international development of the poster art form were mounted by the Walker Art Center in 1984 and by The Museum of Modern Art in 1988.

4. See Helen Farr Sloan, ed., *American Art Nouveau: The Poster Period of John Sloan* (Lock Haven, Pennsylvania: Hammermill Paper Co., 1967); and Anthony Gengarelly and Carol Derby, *The Prendergasts and the Arts & Crafts Movement*, exh. cat. (Williamstown, Massachusetts: Williams College Museum of Art, 1989).

5. Breitenbach and Cogswell, *The American Poster*, p. 13.

6. Little is known of Chéret's early training, except that he apprenticed with a lithography firm at the age of thirteen and that as an artist he was apparently self-taught. He moved to London in 1858 to better his employment opportunities and to learn of advancements in color printing. For the next eight years, he provided designs for a perfume manufacturer who, in 1866, financed his return to Paris to establish a printing firm of his own.

7. See, for example, Poster Auctions International, New York, *Poster Treasures VII*, May 7, 1989, lot 54—six color proofs and the final version of the Chéret poster *Musée Grevin/Pantomimes Lumineuses* of 1892. The sequence of proofs illustrated in the catalogue reveals how Chéret achieved his color effects.

8. Alan Fern, *Word and Image* (New York: The Museum of Modern Art, 1968), p. 12. It would have been difficult indeed for Chéret to have missed the mammoth color woodcut posters of the traveling American circuses. According to circus historian Dick Flint, Curator of Prints and Photographs, Peale Museum, Baltimore, he would have had two opportunities. The American circus of Howes & Cushing was in England from 1858 to 1864, i.e., during Chéret's sojourn in London; and Spalding & Bidwell brought its circus to Paris in 1867, one year after Chéret's return.

9. See Ernest Maindron, *Les Affiches Illustrées* (Paris: H. Launette, 1886, the republication of a series of articles that began in 1884).

10. Phillip Dennis Cate and Sinclair Hamilton Hitchings, *The Color Revolution: Color Lithography in France, 1890–1900*, exh. cat. (New Brunswick, New Jersey: Rutgers University Art Gallery, 1978), p. 10.

11. Fern, *Word and Image*, p. 17.

12. Jacqueline Days Serwer, "The American Poster of the 1890s," Ph.D. dissertation, City University of New York, 1980, p. 64.

13. Elizabeth H. Hawkes, *The Poster Decade: American Posters of the 1890s*, exh. cat. (Wilmington: Delaware Art Museum, 1977), p. 3.

14. See *Catalogue of an Exhibition of Illustrated Bill-Posters*, exh. cat. (New York: Grolier Club, 1890).

15. Brander Matthews, "The Pictorial Poster," *The Century Magazine*, 54 (1892), p. 756.

16. See David Kiehl, "American Art Posters of the 1890s," in *American Art Posters of the 1890s*, p. 13.

17. *The Poster*, 1 (February 1896), n.p.

18. Ibid.

19. See Susan Otis Thompson, *American Book Design and William Morris* (London and New York: R.R. Bowker, 1978).

20. Quoted in Breitenbach and Cogswell, *The American Poster*, pp. 14–15.

21. Quoted in Victor Margolin, *American Poster Renaissance* (New York: Watson-Guptill Publications, 1975), p. 21.

22. Helen S. Hyman, *Design to Persuade: American Literary Advertising Posters of the 1890s*, exh. cat. (New Haven: Yale University Art Gallery, 1978), no. 7.

23. *Poster Lore*, 1 (January 1896), p. 16.

24. See Phillip Dennis Cate, "The French Poster 1868–1900," in *American Art Posters of the 1890s*, pp. 57–72; and Cate and Hitchings, *The Color Revolution*.

25. As has been noted by David Kiehl, Penfield's design for *Harper's/March*, 1897 (cat. 51) is adapted from a four-panel lithograph screen of 1896 by Pierre Bonnard, which was illustrated in *The Studio*, October 1896.

Fig. 35

Louis J. Rhead

LE JOURNAL/de la BEAUTÉ. . . , 1897

Cat. 76

26. Quoted in Serwer, "The American Poster of the 1890s," p. 87.

27. Kiehl, in *American Art Posters of the 1890s*, p. 13.

28. Robert Koch, "Will Bradley and the Art Nouveau Poster," *The Magazine Antiques*, 134 (October 1988), p. 813.

29. Ibid. p. 819.

30. Frank Weitenkampf, *American Graphic Art* (New York: Henry Holt Co., 1912), p. 10.

31. Kiehl, in *American Art Posters of the 1890s*, p. 15.

32. Percival Pollard and Edward Penfield, *Posters in Miniature* (New York: R.H. Russell & Son, 1896), n.p.

33. The etched relief, or line block, was invented by Firmin Gillot in 1850. In the 1870s the firm adapted this process for photography. Line blocks produced by the Gillot method are termed Gillotypes.

34. Will Bradley, "Edward Penfield, Artist," *Bradley: His Book*, 1 (May 1896), pp. 6–7.

35. David Gibson, *Designed to Persuade: The Graphic Art of Edward Penfield*, exh. cat. (Yonkers, New York: The Hudson River Museum, 1984), p. 11.

36. The first issue of *Bradley: His Book* contained an advertisement, designed by Bradley, which declared that "The Photo-Engraving and Electro-typing for this Magazine is done by the Phelps Publishing Company, 27 Worthington Street, Springfield, Mass. Our work suits Mr. Bradley It should suit you."

37. Nancy Finlay, *Artists of the Book in Boston, 1890–1910* (Cambridge, Massachusetts: Harvard College Library, 1985), p. 26.

38. Sinclair Hitchings, "'Fine Art Lithography' in Boston: Craftsmanship in Color, 1840–1900," in *Art & Commerce: American Prints in the Nineteenth Century* (Charlottesville, Virginia: University Press of Virginia, 1978), p. 124.

39. See Nancy Finlay, "American Posters and Publishing in the 1890s," in *American Art Posters of the 1890s*, pp. 50–55.

40. *Poster Lore* (July 1896), cited in Wong, *American Posters of the Nineties*, n.p.

41. Quoted in Margolin, *American Poster Renaissance*, n.p.

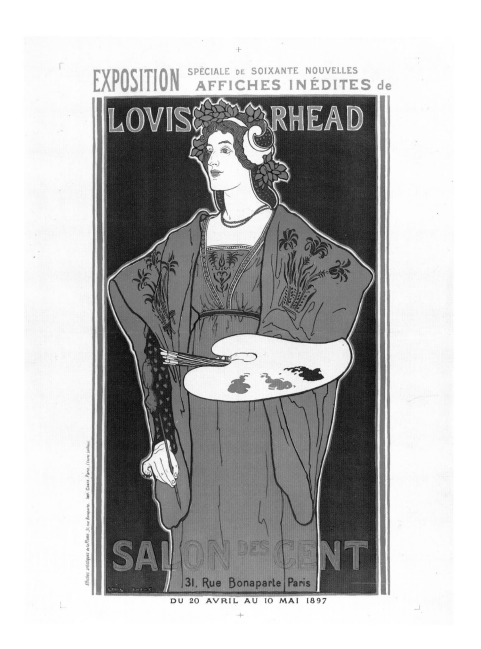

Fig. 36

Louis J. Rhead
EXPOSITION SPÉCIALE. . . , 1897
Cat. 75

Notes to the Catalogue

The catalogue is arranged alphabetically by artist and chronologically within the work of each artist. The title given is exactly as it appears on the poster. A slash indicates the end of a line on the original. The dimensions, given in inches, are those of the image, height preceding width. Each poster is cross-referenced, when possible, to the two standard catalogues for American art posters: Ruth Malhotra, Christina Thom, et al., *Das frühe Plakat in Europa und den USA*, vol. I (Berlin: Gebrüder Mann Verlag, 1973), cited as DFP; and David W. Kiehl, "A Catalogue of American Art Posters of the 1890s," in *American Art Posters of the 1890s in The Metropolitan Museum of Art, including the Leonard A. Lauder Collection* (New York: The Metropolitan Museum of Art, 1987), pp. 97–183, cited as Kiehl. Kiehl's highly annotated listing is extremely informative, the DFP listing less so, but more extensive. Both illustrate all entries, providing the present reader with a source for reproductions of works not illustrated here.

Printing technologies during the nineties were characterized by rapid change as a result of technical advancements and widespread experimentation. Very often the various reproductive and printing processes employed by the artists or their publishers cannot be precisely identified. For this reason, most references to technique have been simplified to either "color lithograph" or "color relief," except in those instances where documentation allows for greater specificity.

That said, most American art posters are color lithographs, and the majority of them were probably printed with zinc plates. Lithographs printed from zinc plates are often indistinguishable from those printed on stone, since metal plates could be mechanically grained to simulate the surface of limestone. By the mid-nineties, zinc had been in use by American lithographers for nearly half a century as a cost-effective substitute for Bavarian limestone. A zinc plate twice the size of a given piece of limestone cost fifty times less and could be stored in one-twentieth the space. Being inexpensive to buy and store, a zinc plate bearing an image could also be put aside in anticipation of successive printings. Zinc plates, mounted on either a flat-bed or rotary press, could be used to print lithographically as well as in relief—that is, negative portions of an image could be bitten with acid, leaving the positive image to be printed in relief.

Some of Edward Penfield's posters (cats. 38, 39) seem to show traces of both planographic and relief printing. The technical rationale may have been that lithography, though it provides smooth color fields, does not carry line work well through long printing runs. Relief processes, by contrast, are ideal for the strong fluid outlines characteristic of the designs of the period, though they print flat areas of color poorly. By the late eighties, both Lautrec and Steinlen were providing designs for Parisian journals in which a key block printed in photorelief provided the outlines for flat color planes printed by stencil. American printers may well have arrived at a similar solution, since the common flat-bed cylinder press could accommodate both planographic and relief print media. More research is needed as to the various technologies employed and the way in which those technologies structured the relationship between artists and printers of the day.

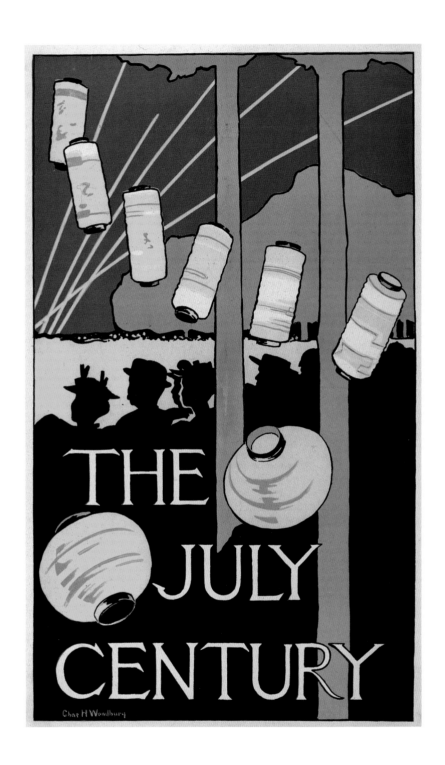

Fig. 37

Charles H. Woodbury
THE/JULY/CENTURY, 1895
Cat. 82

Works in the Exhibition

Will H. Bradley (1868–1962)

Will Bradley's introduction to the printing arts came at the age of eleven, when he became a printer's helper for a weekly newspaper in the northern Michigan town of Ishpeming. He left for Chicago to apprentice as a wood engraver in 1885, but quickly outgrew the position and moved on to work in printing and design as well. By 1889, at the age of twenty-one, he had established himself as a free-lance designer and illustrator. His early work, a series of posters for *The Inland Printer* and *The Chap-Book*, reveals English influences, in particular that of Aubrey Beardsley. Bradley's posters, in their use of flowing line, asymmetrical compositions, and flat contrasting planes of color, represent one of the most potent expressions of Art Nouveau by an American artist.

In late 1894, Bradley moved to Springfield, Massachusetts, to set up his own Wayside Press, in the Kelmscott tradition. His work of the next two years reflects the various stylistic idioms of the Arts & Crafts Movement, which he adopted to the mechanized pressroom with an ease that could only come from complete mastery of the printer's trade. In January 1897, at the age of twenty-eight, he collapsed from overwork and sold his shop to the University Press of Cambridge. In the first decades of this century, he was among the best-paid commercial artists in the country, making significant contributions to the fields of illustration, typography, and commercial design.

1.

THE/CHAP-/BOOK, 1894

Color lithograph, 18⅝ x 12⁷⁄₁₆
Signed (at lower right): BRADLEY
Published by Stone & Kimball, Chicago

References: DFP no. 157; Kiehl no. 14, color pl. 3

Fig. 1

This poster is also known by the title *The Blue Lady* and was Bradley's second design for the Chicago literary magazine *The Chap-Book*.

2.

WHEN HEARTS/ARE TRUMPS/ BY TOM HALL, 1894

Color lithograph, 16⅜ x 13³⁄₁₆
Signed (at middle left):
WILL H BRADLEY
Published by Stone & Kimball, Chicago

References: DFP no. 150; Kiehl no. 15

3.

CHARLES SCRIBNER'S SONS/NEW YORK/THE/MODERN POSTER/ONLY ONE THOUSAND COPIES PRINTED/OF WHICH THIS IS NUMBER 22, 1895

Color relief, 19⁷⁄₁₆ x 12⁷⁄₁₆
Signed in the plate (at upper left):
WILL H. BRADLEY/95; in manuscript (at lower right): C.S.S.
Published by Charles Scribner's Sons, New York

Reference: DFP no. 158

Fig. 2

This poster is numbered in manuscript as 22 out of an edition of 1000. Copies may still be found by the persistent book-fair browser since the poster was originally folded and tucked within the covers of the book—the first American book devoted to the art poster.

4.

MAY/THE CHAP-/BOOK, 1895

Color lithograph, 20 x 13⁵⁄₁₆
Signed (at lower left): BRADLEY
Published by Stone & Kimball, Chicago

References: DFP no. 154; Kiehl no. 18

5.

THE/CHAP-BOOK, 1895

Color lithograph, 20⅝ x 13½
Signed (at upper right):
WILL H/BRADLEY
Published by Stone & Kimball, Chicago

References: DFP no. 156; Kiehl no. 20

This poster is known also as *The Pipes* and was Bradley's fifth design for *The Chap-Book*.

6.

THE/CHAP/BOOK, 1895
Color lithograph, 19¹¹⁄₁₆ x 13⅛
Signed (at lower center): BRADLEY
Published by Stone & Kimball, Chicago

References: DFP no. 153; Kiehl no. 22

Fig. 3

Also known as *Pegasus*, this was
Bradley's sixth design for *The Chap-Book*.

7.

THE CHAP BOOK/THANKSGIVING NO.,
1895
Color lithograph, 19⁹⁄₁₆ x 13³⁄₁₆
Signed (at lower left corner):
WILL H./BRADLEY
Published by Stone & Kimball, Chicago

References: DFP no. 151; Kiehl no. 23,
color pl. 33

Fig. 4

8.

WHITING'S/LEDGER PAPERS/
In their Clear Surface and/in their
Perfect Erasing and/Wearing Qualities
these/are the Finest Papers made/
Ask to have WHITING'S/LEDGERS
used in your/next lot of Blank Books,
1895
Color lithograph on card, 19⅞ x 9¼
Signed (at upper right): BRADLEY
Published by Whiting Paper Company

References: DFP no. 168; Kiehl no. 26

The border design for this poster
generated its nickname, "The Acorns."
The first issue of *Bradley: His Book*
notified readers of the availability of
copies at 75 cents each.

9.

BRADLEY HIS BOOK, 1896
Color woodcut and lithograph,
39¹³⁄₁₆ x 27¹⁄₁₆
Unsigned
Published by The Wayside Press,
Springfield, Massachusetts

References: DFP no. 174; Kiehl no. 30,
color pl. 2

Illus. p. 6

The Kiss, as this poster was known, was
Bradley's first design for a series
advertising his periodical, *Bradley:
His Book*, and is one of the master-
pieces of the American poster movement.

10.

BRADLEY/HIS BOOK/PRICE TEN CENTS/
FOR SALE HERE/JUNE, 1896
Color relief, 18¾ x 8⅝
Signed (at lower left): BRADLEY
Published by The Wayside Press,
Springfield, Massachusetts

References: DFP no. 171; Kiehl no. 31

This was the second poster for
Bradley's magazine and is known also
by the title *The Queen*.

11.

VICTOR/BICYCLES OVERMAN WHEEL
COMPANY/BOSTON NEW YORK
DETROIT DENVER/SAN FRANCISCO
LOS ANGELES PORTLAND ORE/
AGENTI GENERALI PER L'ITALIA/ING.
FERRERO, GATTA-OLIVETTI/TORINO,
1896
Color lithograph, 57⁷⁄₁₆ x 36¾
Unsigned
Published by Overman Wheel Company

References: DFP no. 176 (related);
Kiehl no. 35

Claude Fayette Bragdon (1866–1946)

Born in Oberlin, Ohio, Bragdon was only
nineteen years old when he provided the
first of three poster designs for *The Chap-
Book*. He was also responsible for two
posters for the Rochester *Post Express*,
which garnered the favorable attention of
his contemporaries. He settled in the
Rochester area, and after the turn of
the century practiced architecture,
designed furniture, and was involved in
costume and set design.

12.

THE/Chap-Book/PRICE FIVE CENTS/
Being a MISCELLANY of Curious and/
Interesting Songs, Ballads, Tales, His-/
tories & c; adorned with a variety/of
pictures and very delightful to/read;
newly composed by MANY/
CELEBRATED WRITERS; To which/
are annex'd a LARGE COLLECTION
/of Notices of Books, 1896
Color lithograph, 16¹⁵⁄₁₆ x 12
Signed (at middle right): CB
Published by Stone & Kimball, Chicago

References: DFP no. 185; Kiehl no. 37

Bragdon's second poster for *The Chap-
Book* was the tenth in the series adver-
tising the magazine and is also called
The Carriage.

William L. Carqueville (1871–1946)

Will Carqueville grew up with the smell of printer's ink and the din of the family presses. His family's firm, Shober and Carqueville, was located in Chicago and made a specialty of theater posters. His poster designs for *Lippincott's* and the magazine *International* achieve bold effects with a limited number of colors, a facility born of his experience in commercial printing. Although in America his achievements were overshadowed by those of Edward Penfield and J.J. Gould, he earned considerable attention abroad. In 1896, the year he went to Paris to pursue his studies, ten of his works were included in a major poster exhibition held in Rheims. He returned to Chicago a few years later to continue a career in illustration and design.

13.

LIPPINCOTT'S/JULY, 1895

Color lithograph, 18½ x 12
Signed (at lower right):
WILL CARQUEVILLE
Published by J.B. Lippincott Co.,
Philadelphia

References: DFP no. 201; Kiehl no. 51

Fig. 5

14.

LIPPINCOTT'S/OCTOBER, 1895

Color lithograph, 18⅜ x 11 15/16
Signed (at lower right):
WILL CARQUEVILLE
Published by J.B. Lippincott Co.,
Philadelphia

References: DFP no. 204; Kiehl no. 54

15.

LIPPINCOTT'S/NOVEMBER, 1895

Color lithograph, 18 7/16 x 12
Signed (at lower right):
WILL CARQUEVILLE
Published by J.B. Lippincott Co.,
Philadelphia

References: DFP no. 205; Kiehl no. 55

Fig. 6

Charles Arthur Cox (dates unknown)

Little is known about Charles Cox, who provided a delightful series of posters for the bicycling journal *Bearings*.

16.

BEARINGS/TEN/CENTS, 1896

Color lithograph, 16 x 11
Signed (at lower right): Charles A. Cox
Published by *Bearings*

References: DFP 215; see also Kiehl no. 60

Arthur Wesley Dow (1857–1922)

Dow, an influential painter and teacher at the turn of the century, is best known for his theory of art education based upon Japanese principles of design. Although his involvement in posters was limited to only three or four examples, each provides powerful testimony both to his mastery of color and to the extraordinary talent of his lithographer/translator, Louis Prang.

17.

Modern Art/EDITED BY J.M. BOWLES/
PUBLISHED BY L. PRANG & CO., 1895

Color lithograph, 17¾ x 13 11/16
Signed (at lower left): Arthur W Dow
Printed and published by Louis Prang & Co., Boston

References: DFP no. 217; Kiehl no. 66, color pl. 4

Frontispiece

William Glackens (1870–1938)

Along with his contemporaries John Sloan and Everett Shinn, Glackens began his career as an illustrator for a number of Philadelphia newspapers while studying at the Pennsylvania Academy of the Fine Arts. He contributed at least one design for *Lippincott's* before leaving for Paris to continue his studies. After his return to New York in 1896 he worked as an illustrator, designing at least one more poster, the design included here for *Scribner's*. He went on to achieve considerable recognition as a realist painter of the American urban scene.

18.

SCRIBNER'S/AUGUST/
Fiction Number/ . . . , 1899

Color lithograph, 21⅜ x 13⅝
Signed (at lower left): W. Glackens
Published by Charles Scribner's Sons, New York

References: Not in DFP or Kiehl

19.

Original design for *Scribner's* August Fiction Number, 1899

Pastel and watercolor on paper mounted on board, 21 x 8
Signed (at lower left): W. Glackens

Collection of Leslie and Alice Schreyer

Joseph J. Gould, Jr. (about 1875– about 1935)

Gould, who studied at the Pennsylvania Academy of the Fine Arts, succeeded Will Carqueville as poster designer for the magazine *Lippincott's*, where he worked from 1895 to 1897. Bold, diagonal compositions and the effective use of crayon texture effects characterize the work of this talented artist, who provided covers for *The Saturday Evening Post* after 1900.

20.

LIPPINCOTT'S/FEBRUARY, 1897

Color lithograph, 19 x 11¼
Signed (at upper right): J.J. Gould
Published by J.B. Lippincott Co.,
Philadelphia

References: DFP no. 258; Kiehl no. 89,
color pl. 8

Fig. 7

21.

LIPPINCOTT'S/JULY, 1897

Color lithograph, 16⅞ x 11⁹⁄₁₆
Signed (at upper left): J.J. Gould
Published by J.B. Lippincott Co.,
Philadelphia

Reference: DFP no. 263

Fig. 8

Frank Hazenplug (1873–after 1908)

Frank Hazenplug succeeded Will Bradley as artist for the Chicago firm of Stone & Kimball, providing a series of daring poster designs for their influential journal *The Chap-Book*.

22.

The/Chap-Book, 1895

Color relief, 13¼ x 7⅞
Signed (at lower right): FH
Published by Stone & Kimball, Chicago

References: DFP no. 269; Kiehl no. 97,
color pl. 10

Fig. 9

Also known by the title *The Red Lady*, this was the seventh in the series of posters for *The Chap-Book* and, according to poster historian Jack Rennert, is among the rarest of American art posters.

23.

The Chap-Book, 1896

Color lithograph, 19¹³⁄₁₆ x 13½
Signed (at lower center): FH
Published by Stone & Kimball, Chicago

References: DFP no. 268; Kiehl no. 99

The twelfth *Chap-Book* poster, this is also known by the title *The Black Lady*.

24.

THE/CHAP-/BOOK, 1896

Color lithograph, 20⅜ x 13½
Signed (at middle left): FH
Published by Stone & Kimball, Chicago

Reference: Kiehl no. 100

This poster, also called *The Green Lady*, was Hazenplug's third for *The Chap-Book*.

Herbert Myron Lawrence (1852–1937)

Little is known of Lawrence, who provided four poster designs for The Century Co. The poster exhibited here, done for the October 1895 issue of *The Century Magazine*, shows an awareness of the stylized binding designs of the period by Margaret Armstrong and others.

25.

OCTOBER/CENTURY, 1895

Color relief, 18¾ x 11¼
Signed (at lower left): H M L
Published by The Century Co., New York

References: DFP no. 281; Kiehl no. 111,
color pl. 39

Fig. 10

Florence Lundborg (1871–1949)

Florence Lundborg provided seven poster designs for *The Lark*, a San Francisco humor and literary magazine during the two-year period 1895–97. Her work reveals the influence of her teacher, Arthur F. Mathews, a leader of the Arts & Crafts Movement in California. She composed and cut most of her own designs in wood, achieving a satisfying unity of medium and Japonisme design. After 1900 her career embraced mural painting, book illustration, and portraiture.

26.

What is That/Mother?/THE/LARK/ *My Child*/FOR/AUGUST: 5 CTS, 1895

Color woodcut, 17 x 11½
Signed (at lower left): FL
Published by William Doxey,
San Francisco

References: DFP no. 295; Kiehl no. 117

27.

THE LARK/NOVEMBER, 1895

Color woodcut, 16⅜ x 19¹³⁄₁₆
Signed (at lower right): FL
Published by William Doxey,
San Francisco

References: DFP no. 296; Kiehl no. 118,
color pl. 5

Fig. 11

The landscape depicted features Mt. Tamalpais, which is visible across the bay from San Francisco.

28.

The/LARK/February, 1896

Color woodcut, 19⁵⁄₁₆ x 11⅜
Signed (at lower right): FL del SC
Published by William Doxey,
San Francisco

References: DFP no. 297, Kiehl no. 119

29.

The Lark/for May/THE OREAD, 1896

Color woodcut, 23¾ x 13⅞
Signed (at lower left): FL
Published by William Doxey,
San Francisco

Reference: Kiehl no. 120

30.

THE LARK/AUGUST, 1896

Color woodcut, 16 x 12⅞
Signed (at lower left): del/FL/sc.
Published by William Doxey,
San Francisco

References: DFP no. 298; Kiehl no. 121

Henry McCarter (1865–1943)

McCarter studied at the Pennsylvania
Academy of the Fine Arts and in Paris
before returning to New York to work as a
designer and illustrator for Stone &
Kimball, *Scribner's*, *The Century Magazine*, *Collier's*, and *McClure's*. He taught
at the Pennsylvania Academy of the Fine
Arts and the Art Students League.

31.

SCRIBNER'S/AUGUST/Contains Short
stories-8/pages in color-The Chase of/
Cervera by J.R.Spears-Chap-/ters of
the War by R.H.Davis/FICTION/
NUMBER, 1899

Color lithograph, 22¹¹⁄₁₆ x 13¾
Signed (at center right): HM
Published by Charles Scribner's Sons,
New York

Reference: Carolyn Keay, *American
Posters of the Turn of the Century*
(London: Academy Editions; New York:
St. Martin's Press, 1975), p. 73 illus.

Blanche McManus (1870–?)

McManus began work as an artist and
author in Chicago in 1893, following her
return from art studies in Paris. Her
dramatic design for her own book, *The
True Mother Goose*, makes clever use of
ambiguity between figure and ground.

32.

THE TRUE/MOTHER GOOSE/ WITH
NOTES AND PICTURES BY/
BLANCHE MCMANUS/LAMSON WOLFFE
& CO BOSTON, 1896

Color lithograph, 20⅜ x 14¼
Signed (at middle left): B.MCM.
Published by Lamson Wolffe & Co.,
Boston

References: DFP no. 301; Kiehl no. 127

Fig. 12

Maxfield Parrish (1870–1966)

Maxfield Parrish, whose father was the
painter-etcher Stephen Parrish, studied
at the Pennsylvania Academy of the Fine
Arts. He received many awards for his
poster designs of the nineties, which
included commissions from *Scribner's*,
St. Nicholas, *Harper's Weekly*, *The
Century Magazine*, and the *Ladies Home
Journal*. He went on to become one of the
most popular illustrators and commercial
designers of the early twentieth century.

33.

POSTER SHOW/Pennsylvania/Academy/
of the/Fine Arts/Philadelphia, 1896

Color relief, 30 x 23¾
Signed in block (at lower left): Maxfield/
Parrish; in pencil (at lower right):
Maxfield Parrish
Publisher not indicated

References: Not in DFP or Kiehl

This impression is one of a limited
number signed by the artist for the
collector's market, before the addition
of a separate sheet of letterpress to the
lower margin (for an example of the
double sheet version with letterpress,
see Kiehl no. 133).

34.

THE CENTURY/Midsummer/
Holiday Number./August.
/SECOND PRIZE, CENTURY POSTER
CONTEST./(COPYRIGHT, 1897, BY
THE CENTURY CO.)/ELIHU VEDDER,/
F. HOPKINSON SMITH,/HENRY J.
HARDENBURGH/JUDGES., 1897

Color lithograph, 18⁷⁄₁₆ x 11¹⁵⁄₁₆
Signed (at lower right): Maxfield Parrish
Published by The Century Co., New York

References: DFP no. 317; Kiehl no. 134,
color pl. 13

Fig. 13

35.

SCRIBNER'S/FICTION NUM/BER.
AUGUST, 1897

Color lithograph, 19½ x 14
Signed (at lower right):
MAXFIELD/PARRISH/1897
Published by Charles Scribner's Sons,
New York

References: DFP no. 316; Kiehl no. 135,
color pl. 14

Fig. 14

Collection of Leslie and Alice Schreyer

36.

EXHIBITION OF THE/AMERICAN/
WATER COLOR/SOCIETY/NOW OPEN
AT/NATIONAL ACADEMY OF DESIGN,
1899

Color lithograph, 20⅞ x 13¹⁵⁄₁₆
Signed (at middle left): M.P.
Publisher not indicated

Reference: Coy Ludwig, *Maxfield
Parrish* (New York: Watson-Guptill,
1973), p. 212.

Edward Penfield (1866–1925)

Penfield was born in Brooklyn and studied at the Art Students League. His posters for *Harper's*, designed during his ten-year tenure as art director, are credited with starting the poster craze in America. He provided a number of fine designs advertising the books of Harper and Brothers, and his calendar designs for R.H. Russell and Company (cats. 49A–E) are among the masterworks of his mature style. After 1901, Penfield continued a successful career as a commercial artist.

37.

HARPER'S / FOR / MARCH, 1894

Color lithograph, 15⅞ x 11¹¹⁄₁₆
Signed (at lower right):
EDWARD PENFIELD
Published by Harper and Brothers,
New York

References: DFP no. 330; Kiehl no. 148

38.

HARPER'S / SEPTEMBER, 1894

Color lithograph and relief 16¼ x 10⅝
Signed (at lower left):
EDWARD PENFIELD
Published by Harper and Brothers,
New York

Reference: DFP no. 336; Kiehl no. 153,
color pl. 18

39.

HARPER'S / CHRISTMAS, 1894

Color lithograph and relief 18³⁄₁₆ x 12⅜
Signed (at lower left):
EDWARD PENFIELD
Published by Harper and Brothers,
New York

References: DFP no. 339; Kiehl no. 156

40.

HARPER'S / MARCH, 1896

Color lithograph, 18⅜ x 10¹³⁄₁₆
Signed (at upper left):
EDWARD PENFIELD
Published by Harper and Brothers,
New York

References: DFP no. 354; Kiehl no. 178

Fig. 15

41.

HARPER'S / MAY, 1896

Color lithograph, 17⁹⁄₁₆ x 11¹³⁄₁₆
Signed (at lower right):
EDWARD PENFIELD
Published by Harper and Brothers,
New York

References: DFP no. 356; Kiehl no. 180,
color pl. 43

42.

HARPER'S / JULY, 1896

Color lithograph, 18⅝ x 13¹¹⁄₁₆
Signed (at lower right): [bull's-head logo]
Published by Harper and Brothers,
New York

Reference: See DFP no. 358;
Kiehl no. 182

Fig. 16

Impressions exist in two color variants. This copy, along with the copy in the Lauder Collection at The Metropolitan Museum of Art, has the background printed in green. A copy in the collection of Janet Flint, matching the catalogue listing for this title in DFP, has a background printed in a yellow-beige.

43.

HARPER'S / SEPTEMBER, 1896

Color lithograph, 13¹¹⁄₁₆ x 17⁷⁄₁₆
Signed (at lower right): [bull's-head logo]
Published by Harper and Brothers,
New York

References: DFP no. 360; Kiehl no. 184

44.

HARPER'S / NOVEMBER, 1896

Color lithograph, 17¹³⁄₁₆ x 13⅜
Signed (at upper right): [bull's-head logo] / EDWARD / PENFIELD
Published by Harper and Brothers,
New York

References: DFP no. 362; Kiehl no. 186

Fig. 17

45.

HARPER'S / CHRISTMAS, 1896

Color lithograph, 17³⁄₁₆ x 12⅞
Signed (at upper right):
EDWARD / PENFIELD / [bull's-head logo]
Published by Harper and Brothers,
New York

References: DFP no. 363; Kiehl no. 187

Fig. 18

46.

Ride a / STEARNS / and be / content, 1896

Color lithograph, 54⅝ x 40
Signed (at upper right):
EDWARD PENFIELD
Published by Stearns Manufacturing
Company

Reference: Kiehl no. 190, color pl. 16

Fig. 19

47.

WESTERN / LAWN / 1896 / TENNIS / TOURNAMENT / JULY 11th TO 18th / KENWOOD / COUNTRY / CLUB / 47th ST AND / ELLIS / AVE / CHICAGO, 1896

Color lithograph, 26⅞ x 18⅜
Signed (at lower left):
EDWARD PENFIELD
Publisher not indicated.

Reference: DFP no. 371

Fig. 20

Perhaps the rarest of Penfield posters.

48.
POSTER/CALENDAR/1897/Published
by/R.H. Russell & Son/NEW YORK, 1896

Color lithograph and relief, 13½ x 10
Signed (at upper left):
EDWARD PENFIELD
Published by R.H. Russell & Son,
New York

REF: DFP no. 373; see Kiehl no. 191

Fig. 21

This poster advertised the calendar
that follows (cat. 49A–E).

49.
[Poster Calendar for 1897,
R.H. Russell & Son, New York], 1896

Color lithograph and relief, 13⅞ x 10⅛
Published by R.H. Russell & Son,
New York

References: see DFP no. 373; Kiehl
nos. 191A–E, color pl. 44

This copy, like the copy in the Lauder
Collection at The Metropolitan Museum
of Art, includes a second set of calendar
sheets printed in black and red.

49a.
[Cover] POSTER/CALENDAR/1897/
Published by/R.H. Russell & Son/
NEW YORK

Signed (at upper left corner):
EDWARD PENFIELD

49b.
1897/JANUARY/FEBRUARY/MARCH

Signed (at lower left):
EDWARD PENFIELD

Fig. 22

49c.
APRIL MAY JUNE

Signed (at middle right):
EDWARD PENFIELD

Fig. 23

49d.
JULY AUGUST SEPTEMBER

Signed (at lower left):
EDWARD PENFIELD

Fig. 24

49e.
OCTOBER NOVEMBER DECEMBER

Signed (at lower right): [bull's-head
logo)/EDWARD/PENFIELD

Fig. 25

50.
HARPER'S/FEBRUARY, 1897

Color lithograph and relief, 19 x 13¹⁵⁄₁₆
Signed (at lower right):
EDWARD PENFIELD
Published by Harper and Brothers,
New York

References: DFP no. 373; Kiehl no. 193,
frontispiece

Fig. 27

51.
HARPER'S/MARCH, 1897

Color lithograph, 13¹⁵⁄₁₆ x 19
Signed (at lower left corner):
EDWARD PENFIELD
Published by Harper and Brothers,
New York

References: DFP no. 376; Kiehl no. 194

Fig. 29

Collection of Mr. and Mrs. H. Kurfitz

52.
HARPER'S/APRIL, 1897

Color lithograph, 18³⁄₁₆ x 12¹³⁄₁₆
Signed (at lower left):
EDWARD PENFIELD
Published by Harper and Brothers,
New York

References: DFP no. 377; Kiehl no. 195

53.
HARPER'S/AUGUST, 1897

Color lithograph, 18½ x 13³⁄₁₆
Signed (at lower right):
EDWARD PENFIELD
Published by Harper and Brothers,
New York

References: DFP no. 381; Kiehl no. 199

Fig. 30

54. HARPER'S/FEBRUARY, 1898
Color lithograph, 18¾ x 13³⁄₁₆
Signed (at upper left): EP
Published by Harper and Brothers,
New York

References: DFP no. 387; Kiehl no. 207

55.
HARPER'S/MAY, 1898

Color lithograph, 16 x 9¹⁄₁₆
Signed (at lower left); [bull's-head logo]
Published by Harper and Brothers,
New York

References: DFP no. 390; Kiehl no. 210

56.
[HARPER'S/MAY], 1898

Pencil, pen and ink, ink spatter, and
Chinese white on paper, 16¼ x 9⅝
Unsigned

Color separation for cat. 55.

Anonymous Loan

57.
HARPER'S/NOV'B'R, 1898

Color lithograph, 11⅛ x 18³⁄₁₆
Signed (at lower left): [bull's-head logo]
Published by Harper and Brothers,
New York

References: DFP no. 396; Kiehl no. 216

58.
HARPER'S/JANUARY, 1898

Color lithograph, 11⅛ x 19
Signed (in the horse's harness):
[bull's-head logo]
Published by Harper and Brothers,
New York

References: DFP no. 397; Kiehl no. 217

59.

The/NORTHAMPTON/THE/
NORTHAMPTON CYCLE CO./
NORTHAMPTON, MASS., about 1899

Color lithograph, 39¾ x 26⁵⁄₁₆
Signed (at lower right):
EDWARD PENFIELD
Published by The Northampton Cycle Co.

Reference: Kiehl no. 225, color pl. 53

Fig. 28

Maurice Brazil Prendergast
(1859–1924)

Like other aspiring painters of his day, Prendergast earned a reputation first for his commercial design work, which included four posters, four book cover designs, and three illustrated books during the years 1895–97. His designs, such as the one here for *On the Point*, combine the stylistic elements of both Art Nouveau and the Japanese print. Public recognition of his talent as a painter did not come until the end of the decade.

60.

ON THE POINT/JOSEPH KNIGHT
COMPANY PUBLISHERS./
NATHAN HASKELL DOLE., 1895

Color relief, 12¹⁵⁄₁₆ x 8
Signed (at lower right): MBP
Published by Joseph Knight Co., Boston

Reference: Kiehl no. 230

Ethel Reed (1874–after 1898)

Ethel Reed was only twenty-one when she produced a series of striking designs for *The Boston Herald*, the publishers Lamson, Wolffe & Co., Copeland and Day, and Louis Prang & Co. These works earned her immediate acclaim and established her reputation here and abroad as the pre-eminent female poster artist in America. She was of renowned beauty, and it is said that many of the characters in her posters are self-portraits. She disappeared in 1898 while vacationing in Ireland, and was never heard from again. (See the biographical sketch in The Metropolitan Museum of Art, *American Art Poster of the 1890s*, p. 191.)

61.

ARABELLA AND/ARAMINTA STO-/
RIES BY GERTRU-/DE SMITH WITH/
XV PICTURES BY/ETHEL REED/
BOSTON COPE-/LAND AND DAY/
PRICE $2.00 NET, 1895

Color lithograph, 26 x 14⅜
Signed (at lower right): ETHEL REED
Published by Copeland and Day, Boston

Reference: Kiehl no. 234, color pl. 47

Fig. 31

62.

Albert Morris Bagby's NEW NOVEL/
MISS TRÄUMEREI./
LAMSON, WOLFFE, & CO. 6,
BEACON ST., BOSTON./SOLD HERE
PRICE $1.50, 1895

Color lithograph, 21 x 12⁵⁄₁₆
Signed (at lower right):
ETHEL REED
Published by Lamson, Wolffe, & Co.,
Boston

References: DFP no. 417; Kiehl no. 235

63.

Behind the Arras/by/Bliss Carmen/
Lamson, Wolffe, and Co/Boston and
New York, 1895

Color lithograph, 27⅛ x 17¾
Signed (at middle right): ETHEL REED
Published by Lamson, Wolffe, & Co.,
Boston

References: DFP no. 418; Kiehl no. 236

64.

THE HOUSE OF THE/TREES and other
Poems/ BY ETHELWYN WETHERALD/
PUBLISHED BY LAMSON, WOLFFE/AND
COMPANY, SIX BEACON/STREET,
BOSTON NEW YORK:/LIFE BUILDING/
SOLD HERE,
PRICE, $1.50, 1895

Color relief, 16⅞ x 8
Signed (at lower right): E. REED
Published by Lamson, Wolffe, & Co.,
Boston

References: DFP no. 419; Kiehl no. 237

65.

THE WHITE WAMPUM/ By
E. PAULINE JOHNSON /(Tekahionwake)/
LAMSON, WOLFFE & CO/PUBLISHERS
& IMPORTERS/6 Beacon St., Boston
—Life Building, New-York./
SOLD HERE, 1895

Color relief, 22 x 16½
Signed (at lower center): ETHEL REED
Published by Lamson, Wolffe, & Co.,
Boston

References: DFP no. 424; Kiehl no. 241

66.

THE PENNY/MAGAZINE/SOLD HERE
5CTS,1896

Color relief, 20⅛ x 9¼
Signed (at lower center): ETHEL REED
Published by *The Penny Magazine*,
Philadelphia

Reference: DFP no. 429

67.

In Chilhood's Country/By Louise
Chandler/Moulton Pictur-/ed by
Ethel Reed/Boston: Copeland and/Day
Price $2.00, 1896

Color lithograph, 23½ x 10⅜
Signed (at upper right): ETHEL REED
Published by Copeland and Day, Boston

References: DFP no. 430; Kiehl no. 245,
color pl. 24

Fig. 32

Louis John Rhead (1857–1926)

Born in England, Louis Rhead received his formal training at the South Kensington Art School in London, where he was introduced to the philosophy and aesthetics of the English Arts & Crafts Movement. He came to New York in 1883 to work for *Appleton's*, and soon was managing a busy practice creating designs for the applied arts, following the example of William Morris. He traveled overseas in 1891–94 and met Eugene Grasset in Paris. Grasset's work, which Rhead saw at an exhibition at the Salon des Cent, had a lasting influence on him. They both shared an admiration for the Pre-Raphaelites and the artists Walter Crane and William Morris.

Rhead was the only American to be honored with solo exhibitions in London (1896), and in Paris (1897, at the Salon des Cent). His work was represented by the Parisian print dealers Sagot and Arnould and by the publisher La Plume, who commissioned decorative mural panels from him. He provided designs for *St. Nicholas*, *Scribner's*, *The Century Magazine*, *The Bookman*, and for the publications of Louis Prang & Co. He also received design commissions from a number of newspapers (cat. 69), some of which reached billboard proportions. After 1900, he pursued a career in book illustration.

68.

CENTURY/MAGAZINE/MIDSUMMER HOLIDAY NUMBER THE CENTURY CO. NEW YORK, 1894

Color lithograph, 13⁹⁄₁₆ x 18⁵⁄₁₆
Signed (at lower right): LOUIS RHEAD
Published by The Century Co., New York

Reference: Kiehl no. 249, color pl. 46

Fig. 26

69.

IF YOU SEE IT IN/THE SUN/IT'S SO/READ IT, 1895

Color lithograph, 42⅛ x 27½
Signed (at lower left corner): L.J.R. [monogram]
Published by *The New York Sun*

References: DFP no. 440; Kiehl no. 256

70.

PRANG'S/EASTER/PUBLICATIONS, 1895

Color lithograph, 23¼ x 16⅜
Signed (at lower right): LOUIS/RHEAD
Published by Louis Prang & Co., Boston

References: DFP no. 455; Kiehl no. 258, color pl. 50

Fig. 33

71.

[PRANG'S/EASTER/PUBLICATIONS], 1895

Pencil, ink, and gouache drawing on paper, 14⅛ x 9⁵⁄₁₆
Signed in ink (at lower right): LOUIS RHEAD;
inscribed in pencil on verso: Original Design Invented/by Louis J. Rhead/Flatbush/L.I.

A preparatory sketch for cat. 70

72.

THE CENTURY/FOR/XMAS/CONTAINING/. . ., 1895

Color lithograph, 20½ x 13½
Signed (at lower left): L.J.R.
Published by The Century Co., New York

References: DFP no. 448; Kiehl no. 259

73.

SCRIBNERS/FOR XMAS, 1895

Color lithograph, 17⅛ x 12¾
Signed (at lower right): LOUIS/RHEAD
Published by Charles Scribner's Sons, New York

References: see DFP no. 449 (variant); Kiehl no. 260, color pl. 52

Fig. 34

74.

THE CENTURY/MAGAZINE/FOR/JUNE, 1896

Color lithograph, 20¾ x 10½
Signed (at lower left): LOUIS/RHEAD
Published by The Century Co., New York

References: DFP no. 461; Kiehl no. 265

75.

EXPOSITION SPÉCIALE DE SOIXANTE NOUVELLES AFFICHES INEDITES de/LOUIS RHEAD/SALON DES CENT/31, Rue Bonaparte Paris/DU 20 AVRIL AU 10 MAI 1897, 1897

Color lithograph, 23 x 14½
Signed (at lower left): LOUIS RHEAD
Published by La Plume, Paris

References: DFP no. 468; Kiehl no. 269, color pl. 51

Fig. 36

Louis Rhead was the only American to be given a one-man show at the Salon des Cent, a prestigious venue for poster exhibitions sponsored by the Parisian publisher La Plume.

76.

LE JOURNAL/de la BEAUTÉ/10 Centimes, 1897

Color lithograph, 30⅝ x 58⁷⁄₁₆
Signed (lower left corner): L.J.R. [monogram]
Published by La Plume, Paris

References: DFP no. 454A; Kiehl no. 270

Fig. 35

La Plume commissioned designs for printed mural panels from major poster artists of the day, including Grasset, Mucha, and Rhead. The printer's waste sheets from this run of Rhead's "Peacocks," culled due to misregistration, uneven inking, etc., were given a second life as posters for one of the company's magazines, *Le Journal de la Beauté*, through the simple addition of text.

John Sloan (1871–1951)

Sloan, whose early career in commercial art paralleled that of many of his peers, worked in Philadelphia in the 1890s as a newspaper illustrator. He also provided poster designs for various manufacturers, magazines, and book publishers (cat. 77). He moved to New York in 1904, where he later gained fame as a painter/printmaker of the Ashcan School.

77.

CINDER-PATH TALES/
WILLIAM LINDSEY/BOSTON:
COPELAND AND/DAY PRICE/$1.00, 1896

Color lithograph, 20¹¹⁄₁₆ x 10⅞
Signed (at lower right): John/Sloan
Published by Copeland and Day, Boston

Reference: Kiehl no. 278, color pl. 54

Fig. 38

It has been suggested that Sloan's sprinter is a self-portrait.

John Stewardson (dates unknown)

Stewardson's delightful design for the publisher J.B. Lippincott is our only record of the artist.

78.

THE DRAGON OF WANTLEY/HIS TALE:
BY OWEN WISTER/ILLUSTRATIONS BY
JOHN STEWARDSON, 1895

Color relief, 13⅞ x 10
Unsigned
Published by J. B. Lippincott Co.,
Philadelphia

Reference: Kiehl no. 280

John Henry Twachtman (1853–1902)

Twachtman's single foray into poster design is the work included here. He achieved considerable fame as a landscape painter and was one of the leaders of American Impressionism.

79.

THE DAMNATION OF THERON WARE/
OR ILLUMINATION/BY HAROLD
FREDERIC./PUBLISHED BY
STONE & KIMBALL, 1896

Color lithograph, 20 x 12¹⁄₁₆
Signed (at middle right):
J.H. TWACHTMAN
Published by Stone & Kimball,
New York and Chicago

References: DFP 486; Kiehl no. 282

Robert J. Wildhack (1881–1940)

Wildhack studied under Robert Henri before beginning his career as a painter and illustrator in New York. The poster design exhibited here, while late for the period being surveyed, has been included for its considerable charm.

80.

CENTURY/MAY, 1908

Color lithograph 22¼ x 14⁹⁄₁₆
Signed (at lower right):
[artist's monogram]/WILDHACK
Published by The Century Co., New York

Reference: Carolyn Keay, *American Posters of the Turn of the Century* (London: Academy Editions; New York: St. Martin's Press, 1975), p. 108 illus.

Charles Herbert Woodbury
(1864–1940)

Woodbury received his training at MIT, the Académie Julian in Paris, and in Holland. He is best known as a painter of seascapes, but was also an accomplished designer, etcher, teacher, and writer. The two posters included here are among six he is known to have designed.

81.

SOCIETY OF PAINTERS IN/WATER
COLOR OF HOLLAND./CHASE'S
GALLERY/HAMILTON PLACE BOSTON/
FIRST ANNUAL EXHIBITION/IN THE/
UNITED STATES BEGINNING MARCH
19 '95, 1895

Color lithograph, 19⅜ x 14¼
Signed (at lower left): C.H. Woodbury
Published by Chase's Gallery, Boston

Reference: Kiehl no. 285

82.

THE/JULY/CENTURY, 1895

Color lithograph, 17⅜ x 10¼
Signed (at lower left):
CHAS H WOODBURY
Published by The Century Co., New York

References: DFP no. 501; Kiehl no. 288

Fig. 37

Fig. 38

John Sloan
CINDER-PATH TALES. . . , 1896
Cat. 77

Bibliography

Ades, Dawn. *Posters: The Twentieth-Century Poster, Design of the Avante-Garde* (exhibition catalogue). Minneapolis: Walker Art Center, 1984.

Alexandre, Arsène, M.H. Spielmann, H.C. Bunner, and August Jaccaci. *The Modern Poster*. New York: Charles Scribner's Sons, 1895.

Bradley, Will H. "Edward Penfield, Artist." *Bradley: His Book*, 1 (May 1896), pp. 6–7.

Breitenbach, Edgar, and Margaret Cogswell. *The American Poster*. New York: American Federation of Arts, 1967.

Cate, Phillip Dennis, and Sinclair Hamilton Hitchings. *The Color Revolution: Color Lithography in France 1890–1900* (exhibition catalogue). New Brunswick, New Jersey: Rutgers University Art Gallery, 1978.

Fern, Alan. *Word and Image*. New York: The Museum of Modern Art, 1968.

Finlay, Nancy. *Artists of the Book in Boston, 1890–1910*. Cambridge, Massachusetts: Harvard College Library, 1985.

Gengarelly, Anthony W., and Carol Derby. *The Prendergasts and the Arts & Crafts Movement* (exhibition catalogue). Williamstown, Massachusetts: Williams College Museum of Art, 1989.

Gibson, David. *Designed to Persuade: The Graphic Art of Edward Penfield* (exhibition catalogue). Yonkers, New York: The Hudson River Museum, 1984.

Grolier Club, New York. *Catalogue of an Exhibition of Illustrated Bill-Posters* (exhibition catalogue). New York: Grolier Club, 1890.

Hawkes, Elizabeth H. *The Poster Decade: American Posters of the 1890s* (exhibition catalogue). Wilmington: Delaware Art Museum, 1977.

Hillier, Bevis. *Posters*. New York: Stein & Day, 1969.

Hitchings, Sinclair Hamilton. "'Fine Art Lithography' in Boston: Craftsmanship in Color, 1840–1900." In *Art & Commerce: American Prints of the Nineteenth Century*. Charlottesville, Virginia: University Press of Virginia, 1978.

Hyman, Helen S. *Design to Persuade: American Literary Advertising Posters of the 1890s* (exhibition catalogue). New Haven: Yale University Art Gallery, 1978.

Keay, Carolyn. *American Posters of the Turn of the Century*. New York: St. Martin's Press, 1975.

Koch, Robert. "Will Bradley and the Art Nouveau Poster." *The Magazine Antiques*, 134 (October 1988), p. 813.

Maindron, Ernest. *Les Affiches Illustrées*. Paris: H. Launette, 1886.

Malhotra, Ruth, Christina Thom, et al. *Das frühe Plakat in Europa und den USA*. Vol. I. Berlin: Gebrüder Mann Verlag, 1973.

Margolin, Victor. *American Poster Renaissance*. New York: Watson-Guptill Publications, 1975.

Matthews, Brander. "The Pictorial Poster." *The Century Magazine*, 54 (1892), pp. 748–56.

Mayor, A. Hyatt. *Prints & People: A Social History of Printed Pictures*. New York: The Metropolitan Museum of Art, 1971.

The Metropolitan Museum of Art, New York. *American Art Posters of the 1890s in The Metropolitan Museum of Art, including the Leonard A. Lauder Collection*. New York: The Metropolitan Museum of Art, 1987. Essays: David W. Kiehl, "American Art Posters of the 1890s," pp. 11–20; Nancy Finlay, "American Posters and Publishing in the 1890s," pp. 45–55; Phillip Dennis Cate, "The French Poster 1868–1900," pp. 57–72; David W. Kiehl, "A Catalogue of American Art Posters of the 1890s," pp. 97–183.

Pollard, Percival, and Edward Penfield. *Posters in Miniature*. New York: R.H. Russell & Son, 1896.

Serwer, Jacqueline Days. "The American Poster of the 1890s." Ph.D. dissertation. City University of New York, 1980.

Sloan, Helen Farr, ed. *American Art Nouveau: The Poster Period of John Sloan*. Lock Haven, Pennsylvania: Hammermill Paper Co., 1967.

Thompson, Susan Otis. *American Book Design and William Morris*. London and New York: R.R. Bowker, 1978.

Weitenkampf, Frank. *American Graphic Art*. New York: Henry Holt Co., 1912.

Wong, Roberta Waddell. *American Posters of the Nineties* (exhibition catalogue). Boston: Boston Public Library, et al., 1974.

———. *Will H. Bradley: American Artist and Craftsman (1868–1962)* (exhibition catalogue). New York: The Metropolitan Museum of Art, 1972.

———, and Clarence P. Hornung. *Will Bradley: His Graphic Art*. New York: Dover Publications, 1974.

2500 COPIES

Designed by Elizabeth Finger

Text set in Monotype Walbaum with hand-set display typography
by Michael and Winifred Bixler, Skaneateles, New York

Printed on Cameo 100# dull text paper
by Meridian Printing, East Greenwich, Rhode Island

Bound by The Riverside Group, Rochester, New York

Cover embossed and stamped on Curtis Tweedweave

All photographs are by Helga Photo Studio

Edited by Sheila Schwartz